Journey to a Better World

Bully Blues

Seth walked down the hall...

... and puffed out his chest.

Starting in on the thing that he did best...

... he yelled to Lorenzo, who had transferred this year, "Go back to your country! You don't belong here!"

The kids looked excited. Some clapped and cheered.

Except for the one that was typically feared.

Seth rolled his eyes and said, "I don't care! For all that I know, you were better off there!"

He scowled and hurried to gather his stuff and stormed off in an angry huff.

Abdi drew a picture for all to see and labeled it "My Family Tree."

Each student grabbed a colored thread and moved according to what was said.

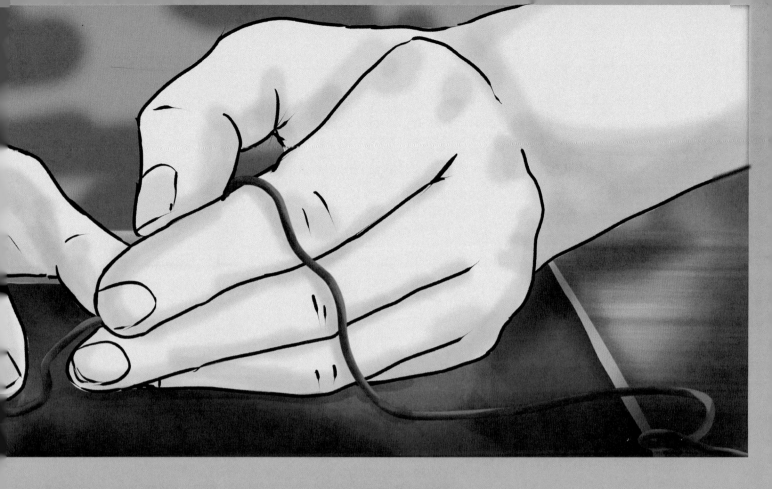

"My parents were born in the same place as you!" José said while grabbing the thread that was blue.

"You have much in common," Abdi said while he viewed overlapping threads.

Let's Experiment!

What's your heritage?

Follow this lab and you'll be able understand your heritage and others' just like Seth and Abdi!

Overview

In this lab, we will be retracing your family's lineage and also learning about your peers' family lineage as we explore your family's "roots." The goal is to learn more about where we come from, understand our own unique family history and culture, and learn about the unique and rich culture of those around us!

Supplies Needed

Don't worry about needing anything super specific or fancy. This exercise can be done anywhere because it uses simple supplies and knowledge about your family's history!

Five different colored markers or pencils: red, green, blue, orange, yellow, and purple

Beginning Set-Up

Using the diagram on the next page, fill in your family tree and then answer the following questions about you and your family's culture and roots!

Be sure to read the directions on each page *carefully* to avoid any confusion or mistakes!

Western Hemisphere

North America

Equator

South America

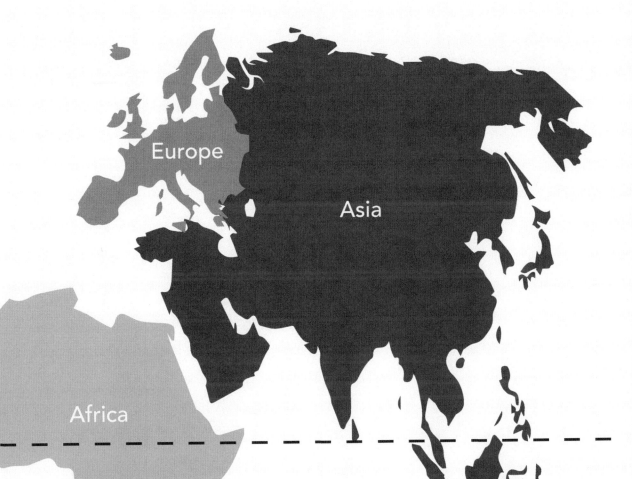

Europe

Asia

Africa

Australia

Part 01: Your Family Heritage

Using the map from the previous page, color in the dots next to your ancestor's name according to where they were born.

Ex: One of Jericho's great-grandfathers was born in France, so Jericho would color in the circle by his great-grandfather's name orange because Europe is orange on the map.

Parent/Guardian 01

○ _____
Great-Grandparent

○ _____
Great-Grandparent

○ _____
Grandparent

○ _____
Grandparent

○ _____
Parent/Guardian

○ _____
You

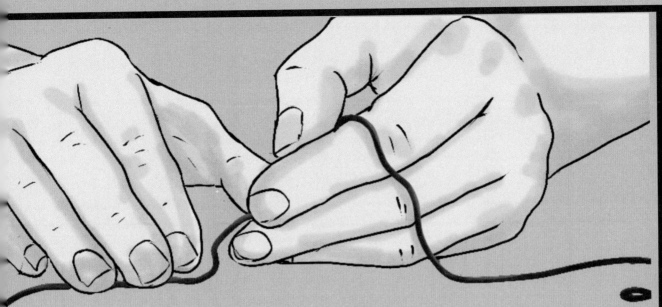

○ _____
Great-Grandparent

○ _____
Great-Grandparent

○ _____
Grandparent

○ _____
Grandparent

○ _____
Parent/Guardian

○ _____
You

SCAN ME

Part 02: My Peers' Families

Using your ancestral chart, compare your chart to your classmates' charts to answer the questions below!

A. Are there others in your class that have come from the same continent?

◯ Yes ◯ No

If yes, how many? _____

B. Are there others in your class that have come from the same country as your family?

◯ Yes ◯ No

If yes, how many? _____

C. What kind of food comes from your family's country that you would like to try?

Answer: _____

_____

_____

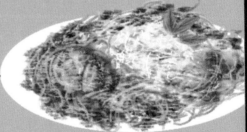

D. What kind of food would you like to try from someone else's country?

Answer: _____

_____

_____

Part 02: My Peers' Families

Compare Classroom Families

Using the information you just gathered, you will compare your graph to your classmates' graphs three times. The first round of comparisons, you will stand:
→ Next to someone whose parent/guardian is from the same continent

On the second round of comparisons, you will stand:
→ Next to someone whose grandparent is from the same continent

On the third and final round, you will stand:
→ Next to someone whose great grandparent is from the same continent

Final Questions

1. Did the groups get bigger the further down the parent/guardian, grandparent, great-grandparent line you went?

_____
_____
_____
_____
_____

2. Do you have more classmates that have similar ancestral "roots" than you thought you did?

_____
_____
_____
_____
_____

The very next day, there was one empty chair. They called out names, and Seth wasn't there.

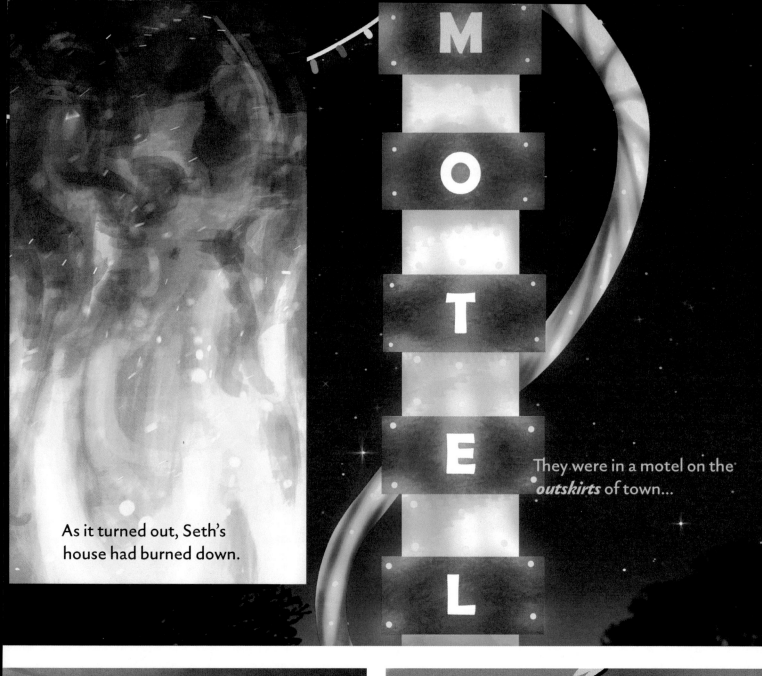

M
O
T
E
L

They were in a motel on the *outskirts* of town...

As it turned out, Seth's house had burned down.

... with nothing to wear but the clothes on their backs...

and nothing to eat except for small snacks.

Abdi had an idea and it seemed rather grand! They could work on a schedule of meals that were planned.

"If we all take turns making dinner each night, I think, Seth's family might be alright. Who'd like to join me?

It's the right thing to do, even if he would not do this for you."

Seth's family was shocked at the *gracious* invite...

... and went to Lorenzo's the very first night.

They welcomed them in...

... the table was set...

... and covered in foods that they hadn't tried yet.

"Here, have a seat,"
Lorenzo's mom said.
"We have *beef bolognese*
and freshly baked bread."

BEEF BOLOGNESE

*Dish may contain allergens

Culture

Italy has a very rich *culture*, steeped in arts, architecture, music, and food. As the birth-place of the Roman Empire, Roman Catholic Church, and Italian Renaissance, Italy's culture has evolved through the ages and flourishes to this day. Family gatherings are central to Italian culture, and oftentimes food plays a major role in such events.

Ingredients

- 1 ½ tbsp olive oil
- 2 garlic cloves, minced
- 1 onion, finely chopped (brown, yellow or white)
- 1 lb beef minced (ground beef) OR half pork, half beef
- ½ cup water or beef broth
- 2 beef bouillon cubes, crumbled OR granulated beef bouillon
- 28 oz can crushed tomatoes
- 2 tbsp tomato paste
- 2 tsp white sugar , if needed
- 2 tsp Worcestershire sauce
- 2 dried bay leaves
- 2 sprigs fresh thyme (or ½ tsp dried thyme or oregano)
- Salt and pepper
- Spaghetti
- Parmesan cheese

Geography

Italy is a *country* in the Northern and Eastern *hemispheres* located on the *continent* of Europe. It is a peninsula nation with mountains and various climates, providing the perfect conditions for different cuisines, including potatoes, pork, beef, fish, rice, olives, tomatoes, garlic, artichokes, eggplant, and various cheeses.

José was the host of night number two...

He cooked up *pozole*, his favorite stew!

POZOLE

Culture

Mexico is a Hispanic country with Aztec, Mayan, and Spanish influences. Mexico has a colorful and flourishing society that honors traditions, celebrates family, and is known for folk art derived from indigenous and Spanish crafts.

Ingredients

- 3 lb. pork shoulder, cut into 2" pieces
- Kosher salt
- Freshly ground black pepper
- 1 large yellow onion, quartered
- 3 cloves garlic, sliced
- 1 tsp. cloves
- 1 tsp. cumin seeds
- 1 bay leaf
- 4 cups low-sodium chicken broth
- 2 dried chiles de arbol, stem and seeds removed
- 2 dried ancho chiles, stem and seeds removed
- 2 dried guajillo chiles, stem and seeds removed
- 3 (15-oz.) cans hominy, drained and rinsed

Geography

Mexico is a Hispanic country found in the Western and Northern hemispheres located on the continent of North America. The nation has everything from high mountains to deep canyons, sweeping deserts to low coastal plains, and dense rainforests. This varied climate provides perfect conditions to grow many foods, such as corn, rice, avocados, beans, barley, coffee, lemons, limes, and other tropical fruits.

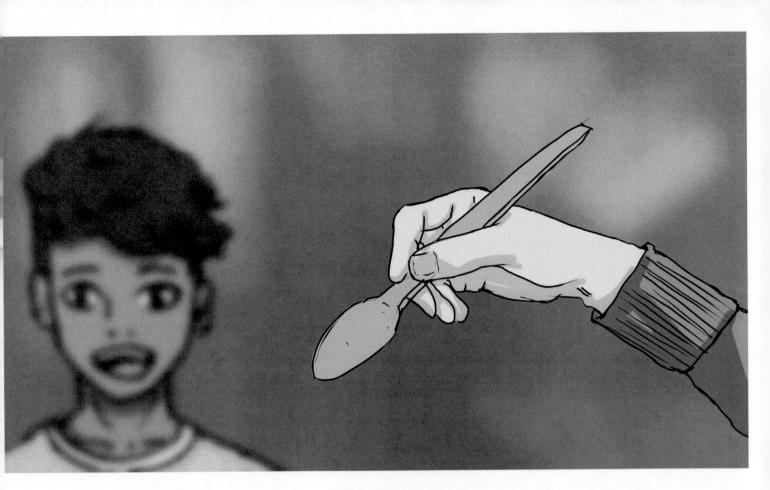

Though dinner was great, something was wrong.

Seth kept his head down all night long.

Aadhil's family hosted night number three.

They served *dates, samosas*, and cups full of tea.

SAMOSAS & DATES

*Dish may contain allergens

Ingredients

- 1 ½ cups Beluga lentil soaked overnight
- 1½ cups Puy lentils
- 4 jalapenos (finely diced)
- 4 onions (finely diced)
- 3 cloves garlic (finely diced)
- 1 cup cilantro (finely chopped)
- 1 teaspoon cardamom seeds (crushed)
- ½ teaspoon cinnamon
- salt (to taste)
- 1 teaspoon black pepper
- 10 spring roll sheets
- Olive oil (for frying)
- 1 cup of dates

Culture

Ethiopia is a multi-cultural country comprised of various ethnicities, backgrounds and religious beliefs. There are over eighty different languages spoken in Ethiopia, with English being the most commonly spoken foreign language. Ethiopians are well-known for their friendliness as well as rich cultural traditions and music.

Geography

Ethiopia is a country located in the Southern and Eastern Hemispheres on the continent of Africa. Its geography ranges from flat plateaus to mountains, deep gorges, to river valleys. The Ethiopian Highlands cover most of the country, with elevation levels between 6,562–8,202 feet above sea level. The country's main agricultural products are coffee, corn, beans, wheat, oilseeds, and sugarcane.

Aadhil's father said, "I don't mean to be rude. Is something the matter? You've not touched your food."

"I've been mean to Aadhil," Seth said with a sigh. "You've been nice to me, and I just don't know why."

"Our differences are what make us great.

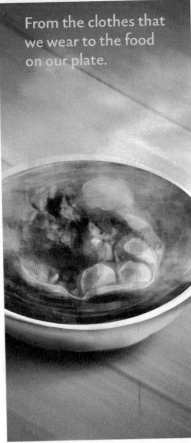

From the clothes that we wear to the food on our plate.

But there is one thing that we certainly share. We are all human and deserve love and care."

Abdi came by with news to share. He had organized a cultural fair.

He needed some help to get it all ready and worked with his friend, Dr. Sabeti.

There were tables set up around the town square.

Each family brought food and items to share.

There was singing and dancing out in the street.

And they met people they'd never gotten to meet.

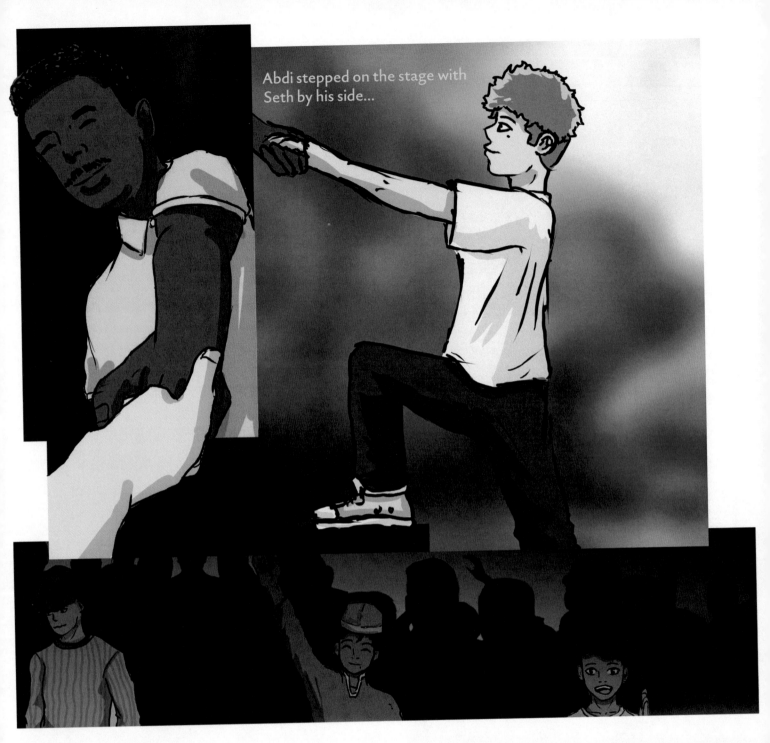

Abdi stepped on the stage with Seth by his side...

And presented a box...

... with money inside.

"Our differences are what make us unique. From the food we prepare...

... to the language we speak.

We would like to present this money to you...

... to rebuild your house and furnish it too!"

From that day forward, Seth changed his ways and hosted future Cultural Days.

His appreciation for other cultures grew. And he even learned a new language or two.

Process Notes

Terms and Definitions

Outskirts: the outer parts of a town or city

 → outskirts

Gracious: courteous, kind, and pleasant

Culture: the traditions, arts, and achievements of a particular nation, people or other social group

ex: Hispanics have a culture based on family strength
: Jazz comes from African American culture

Beef Bolognese: Italian meal made with meat that is then mixed with pasta before eating

Poloze: meal that is traditional soup or stew from Mexican cuisine

Dates: Northern Africa, the Middle East, and South Asia flowering plant farmed for its edible sweet fruit

date palm ———→ dates

Samosas: South Asian fried or baked pastry with a tasty filling like spiced potatoes, onions, peas, chicken and other meats, or lentils that come in different shapes like triangles, cones, or half-moon shapes

Hemisphere: a half of the earth, usually as divided into northern and southern halves by the equator, or eastern and western halves by the imaginary line passing through the poles

N ——— equator   W   E
        S

Continent: any of the world's permanent areas of land
ex: Africa, Antartica, Asia, Australia, Europe, North America, South America

Country: a nation with its own government that occupies a particular territory
ex: USA, China, South Africa, Japan, Nigeria, Columbia, Vietnam, England, France

Map of Amica County

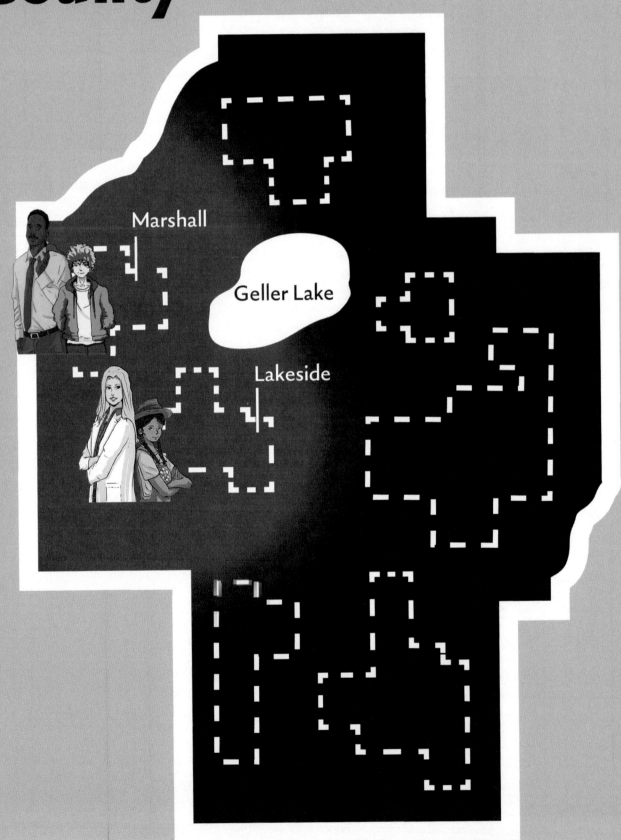

Marshall

Geller Lake

Lakeside

The adventure continues in Book 3!

See if you can find the cameo appearance of Book 3's mentor figure from the clue below!

Hey, Seth here! Book 3's mentor visits us in the scene beside me. Best of luck finding her!

Book 3's mentor visits our heroes in this scene. Can you guess who it is?

Find out who the mystery mentor is and how they help our next hero as you follow along the *Journey to a Better World* book series!

Born in Mogadishu to nomadic parents, Abdi Nor Iftin survived famine, war, and child soldiering, Thanks to the movies available to him, he taught himself English by watching American action films. By repeating and imitating the carefree actors, he earned himself the nickname "Abdi American." Through guerilla journalism, Abdi dispatched stories about his life to a series titled Messages from Mogadishu on American Public Media. His stories were short listed for Peabody Awards in 2016. These stories were later picked by NPR, the BBC and later This America.

After surviving a bombing at his house one evening in 2009, Abdi finally said goodbye to his home country and moved to Kenya where he and his brother lived as refugees. In an amazing stroke of luck, he won entrance to the U.S. in August 2014, in the annual visa lottery, though his route to America — ending in a harrowing sequence of events that nearly stranded him in Nairobi — did not come easily.

Now a best-selling and award-winning author based in the state of Maine; featured on CNN, NPR, NYT, Washington Post, The Boston Globe, Abdi is an advocate for refugee and immigrant rights. He is dedicated to bringing people together through his stories of survival and resilience.

ABDI NOR IFTIN

Tracy Blom is a best-selling author with over twenty published titles in bookstores, museums, zoos, airports, and major retailers across the United States.

Every book she has ever created first began as a dream, written and recorded in one of many dream journals. Dreams are the common thread that wind between her stories, and for a long time, was perplexing to even her. Over time, she came to understand and cherish the gift of nightly vision and went on to create fairytales, young adult novels, and lighthearted picture books.

If you look closely, you can decode the underlying messages in her work, most of which encourage readers to believe in themselves, embrace their differences as gifts, and make the world a better place.

Amidst the challenges of 2020, Tracy created her first theatrical play, which is currently under consideration by the Cincinnati Ballet, published her first para-normal thriller, and began a series of environmental, STEM books addressing critical topics including climate change, cleaning up the ocean, and creating innovative ways to repurpose items.

Her mission is to create books of change, inspire future generations, and be a sounding board for gifted children who may not feel like they belong.

TRACY BLOM

Ronald Mckinney, Studio Art BFA (2022), Louisiana Tech University

Ronald Mckinney is currently a senior at Louisiana Tech University studying studio art. He graduated from Captain Shreve High School in 2018 with a focus in engineering but, during his senior year, had a realization that his passion was in the arts.

In addition to the Inspire Project's Journey to a Better World series, he is completing his senior thesis project *The Light of the World* which is a visual re-telling of the Gospels in a cinematic illustrative narrative. After graduation, he would like to be a full time illustrator working in the concept art realm or to continue to work on book illustrations. He hopes to continue to make art that inspires others and creates a positive impact in the world through art.

His portfolio can be found on Instagram: @mcrondoart.

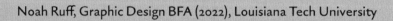

RONALD MCKINNEY

Noah Ruff, Graphic Design BFA (2022), Louisiana Tech University

Noah Ruff is a graphic design student based in Ruston, Louisiana. He moved to Ruston in 2011 from Midland, Texas, and graduated from Ruston High School in the spring of 2018. Noah currently goes to Louisiana Tech University with plans to attend graduate school at Texas A&M.

Aside from the Inspire Project's Journey to a Better World, he has designed various T-shirts and other materials for his fraternity chapter Beta Upsilon Chi and has produced multiple designs for the Ruston business FYZICAL Therapy and Balance Centers.

His portfolio can be found on Instagram: @noah_ruff41.

NOAH RUFF

What is the Inspire Project?

THE
Inspire
PROJECT

About Inspire Project

The Inspire Project is a free program that began in 2017 connecting students with amazing people worldwide to have meaningful discussions about our guest's lives, careers, dealing with failure, success, and many other facets of life. Inspire's format is a dialogue-driven discussion with students. Think of it as a fireside chat, minus the fire. No pomp and circumstance, just students talking with amazing people.

Phineas and Ferb creator Dan Povenmire

Music legend Garth Brooks

Award-winning actress Jada Pinkett Smith

Louisiana Tech University

For 125 years, Louisiana Tech University has been providing a unique educational experience to students. Tech is committed to quality in teaching, research, creative activity, public service, and workforce and economic development. The University's graduates have gone on to greatness including work:

- Helping our nation be the first to land on the moon
- Leading global companies in energy production and transportation
- Securing and defending our nation from global threats
- Saving lives through medical and biomedical discoveries and treatments
- Leading entrepreneur business development and Fortune 100 companies
- Educating and inspiring future generations

What is the VISTA Program?

Established in 2015, the Visual Integration of Science Through Art (VISTA) Center at Louisiana Tech University uses an interdisciplinary approach to teach students how to combine science and art in ways that lead to successful careers and important contributions to society.

Offering minors in undergraduate, minors in pre-medical illustration, and scientific visualization, students have the opportunity to use knowledge gained in a science-based curriculum, techniques learned in art courses, and professional skills developed through client-based projects. These experiences prepare them for a range of careers in visual communication, health, medicine, and research. VISTA Center Directors Nick Bustamante and Dr. Jamie Newman serve as Art and Content Directors for the Inspire Project's *Journey to a Better World* series.

For more information visit **latech.edu** and **latechvista.com**

Printed in the United States of America
First Printing, 2022

Made in the USA
Coppell, TX
21 April 2022

76887792R00031